This book belongs to

....

As the moon rises and casts its ethereal light across the characters captured in the pages of this book it reveals a night alive with mischief. Watch the shadows as you tiptoe through this moonlit collection of pen-and-ink illustrations all waiting to be brought to life through color.

This book contains 25 original hand-drawn illustrations for you to color.

For artists, coloring enthusiasts, and the mischievous of all ages!

See more at rjhampson.com

 **russelljamesart**

Published by Hop Skip Jump
PO Box 1324 Buderim Queensland Australia 4556

First published 2023.
Copyright © 2023 R.J. Hampson.

ISBN: 978-1-922472-19-9

Using this book

Find a quiet place away from distractions.
Relax and immerse yourself in the process of coloring
as you explore the details of each illustration.

This book is best suited to color pencils or markers.
Wet mediums should be used sparingly. Slide a card or sheets
of paper behind the illustration you are coloring to avoid
marker bleed through.

Find fresh coloring pages by signing up to Russell's
newsletter. Get free downloadable pages and updates on
new books at -

rjhampson.com

DRAGON IN THE MIST

BUSTED

THE SLEEPING TREE

THE TEMPLE GATE

WILD RIDE

MIDNIGHT MAYHEM

THE LAST MILE

LARRY VISITS THE ORACLE

STAR CATCHER

TERRARIUM

BABYSITTING

FOREST KING

GUARDIANS

JUNGLE NIGHTS

THE OBSERVATORY

THE GREAT ESCAPE

YE OLD HUNT

YE OLD HUNT

MOM, I'M HUNGRY

THINGS THAT GO BUMP IN THE NIGHT

SPACE WALK

SOMETHING UNDER THE BED

THE CELLIST

SMUGGLERS ISLAND

SKY PIRATE

THE STING IN THE TALE

Searching for more?

Find new coloring pages by signing up to R.J. Hampson's newsletter.
Get free downloadable pages, monthly coloring sheets,
and updates on new books at -
rjhampson.com/coloring

Thanks for choosing this coloring book.
If you enjoyed it, please consider leaving a review.
It will help to let more people in on the experience
plus you'd certainly make this illustrator very happy!

Published books in this series

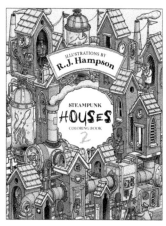

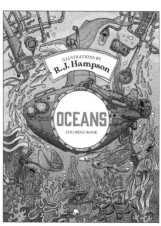

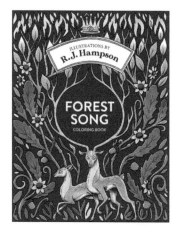

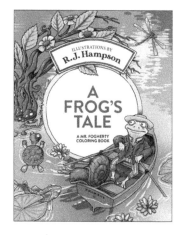
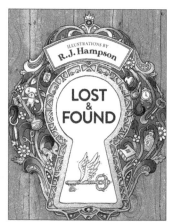

See flip-throughs and new releases at **rjhampson.com**

Printed in the USA
CPSIA information can be obtained
at www.ICGtesting.com
LVHW071537061023
760261LV00013B/638